I Am a Person

by
Sarah Pirtle

Macmillan/McGraw-Hill
School Publishing

New York □ Chicago □ Columbus

I am a person, like no other,
Like no other, plant or animal.

I shout with glee!

I am me, whoa, I am me!

And I'm glad it's true
You are you, whoa,

You are you!

I am me!
You are you!

8